Gratitude journal

This book belongs to:

_____

Gratitude Journal

First Edition: 2022©
ISBN: 978-987-48921-3-3

Diary, Gratitude, Journal, Self Help, Appreciation
Women, Positive Thinking, Emotions, Self Control, Healing

Author:Escribirte
Publisher: A. M. Rothman
Design: A.M. Rothmann
Publisher: escribirte.com.ar

This book was created in collaboration
with Professor Celina Emborg,
a specialist in Art and Health.

How to use this diary?

The Gratitude Journal, A Guided Journey, is designed to guide you so using this gratitude map is a breeze. Just follow the arrows and complete. With only 5 minutes you can change your life.

First things first, do the activity every day for at least 21 weeks. The most important thing is to have the consistency and perseverance to do it every day.

If you feel very negative, try to complete it by finding the people and situations that give you pleasure, helped you during the day, or in your life.

For example:
- of you, of your character, personality or physique.
- from your friends or your family.
- of your life.
- from your house or where you live.
- about your work, or what you do
- things you have experienced today.
- people you have had in your life.
- experiences you have lived.
- things you have (possessions).
- things that have been difficult in your life, and that you have overcome
- things you have learned, skills, etc.
- opportunities, that you have had or lost.

If it doesn't occur to you, or you think you don't have anything to Thanks, you can write simple and obvious things. For example, thanks that I can breathe, thanks that I have good health, thank you that I have food, even thank you i'm alive. This is also very important, and is a great starting point.

If you are already in a more advanced stage, and you feel happier and more grateful, I recommend you reflect and stay in the feeling for a few moments.

In other words, instead of just writing, stay feeling and thanking this for a few minutes.

This is a great way for your body to adopt this good feeling more regularly.

A very important detail, at the time of writing is uses positive words, different studies indicate that happiness increases more rapidly when use positive words, instead of negative words. For example, thanks because I have good health, It's better than thanks that we're not sick.

Another important detail is, complete this diary before to go to sleep, and do it without interruptions. Where you can dedicate 5 minutes to reflect without being bothered.

It is recommended to do it before going to sleep to leave with the thought and emotion of gratitude in the body and mind. Which will improve your sleep, and encouragement for the next day.

Very important, if you feel invaded by the negative thoughts use this gratitude journal, instead of letting yourself be carried away by your head.

This will help guide your attention and focus on what really important. That's why every time you're invaded negative thoughts, use this map to guide your thinking

Why is this book important?

The Gratitude Journal, is a tool for achieving the happiness, health, and success you've always wanted. In this diary you will find different exercises and activities, in the form of a map, that will lead you to work with gratitude, appreciation and positive thinking. The exercises on this book was created with Prof. Celina Emborg, a specialist in Art and Health.

When we cultivate gratitude, we change the way we feel, and this changes the way we think and act. Therefore, our results change. Different studies have verified that when we think negatively, or get angry we become dumber, because our IQ, which means that we don't see things clearly, we react badly, and that we don't. Let's see the opportunities we have.

By letting go of anger, we think more clearly, see possibilities we didn't see before, which prevents frustration and brings about more achievement and personal power. Less anger and more joy.

Gratitude recharges energy, increases self-esteem, it encourages us, in addition to producing peace and mental clarity, which is related to physical, mental and spiritual well-being. Thus, gratitude leads us directly to happiness, success and a full life. It is the best antidote against anger, frustration, envy and resentment.

Date:

Start here

Today I am grateful for:

I feel blessed because

I love being:

I love my life and I am happy because:

I would like to:

That's why Thanks the Universe/God to:

Thanks!

Date:

Today I am grateful for:

Start here

10 things I am thankful for:

I feel blessed to be:

Thanks to _____

I love my life and I am happy that:

Thanks!

I feel very blessed to have:

_____

_____

_____

_____

Other things that I have in my heart
that make me feel happy and blessed

_____

_____

_____

_____

_____

_____

_____

Thanks

Thanks, thanks, thanks

Thanks...

_____

_____

_____

_____

_____

_____

_____

_____

_____

_____

_____

Reflect and be thankful for those little things you
have in your life that you take for granted.

Date:

Start here

Today I want to say thanks (God / Universe) that:

_____

_____

_____

_____

Thanks for: _____

_____

_____

_____

_____

_____

_____

My to-do list which
I am grateful to have:

In my life I am grateful for...

Thanks

I feel very blessed because I learned:

People I have in my heart
that make me feel happy and blessed

Thanks,
thanks,
thanks

Thanks

I Wish...

Thank someone who has been in your life:

Date:

Start here

Things I am grateful for:

Thanks!

Date:

Start here

Today I am grateful for:

I feel blessed because

I love being:

I love my life and I am happy because:

I would like to:

That's why Thanks the Universe/God to:

Thanks!

Date:

Start here

Today I am grateful for: _____
_____
_____
_____

10 things I am thankful for:

I feel blessed to be:
_____
_____
_____
_____
_____
_____
_____
_____

Thanks to _____

I love my life and I am happy that:
_____
_____
_____
_____

Thanks!

I feel very blessed to have:

_____

_____

_____

Other things that I have in my heart
that make me feel happy and blessed

_____

_____

_____

_____

_____

_____

Thanks

Thanks, thanks, thanks

Thanks...

_____

_____

_____

_____

_____

_____

_____

_____

_____

_____

Reflect and be thankful for those little things you
have in your life that you take for granted.

Date:

Start here

Today I want to say thanks (God / Universe) that:

_____

_____

_____

Thanks for: _____

_____

_____

_____

_____

_____

_____

_____

In my life I am grateful for...

My to-do list which I am grateful to have:

Thanks

I feel very blessed because I learned:

_____

_____

_____

_____

People I have in my heart
that make me feel happy and blessed

Thanks,
thanks,
thanks

Thanks

I Wish...

_____

_____

_____

_____

_____

_____

_____

_____

_____

_____

_____

Thank someone who has been in your life:

Date:

Start here

Things I am grateful for:

Thanks!

Date:

Today I am grateful for:

I feel blessed because

I love being:

I love my life and I am happy because:

I would like to:

That's why Thasks the Universe/God to:

Thanks!

Date: _____

Start here

Today I am grateful for: _____
_____
_____
_____

10 things I am thankful for:
_____
_____
_____
_____
_____
_____
_____
_____

I feel blessed to be:
_____
_____
_____
_____
_____
_____
_____

Thanks to _____
_____
_____
_____
_____
_____

I love my life and I am happy that:
_____
_____
_____
_____

Thanks!

I feel very blessed to have:

_____

_____

_____

_____

Other things that I have in my heart
that make me feel happy and blessed

_____

_____

_____

_____

_____

_____

Thanks...

_____

_____

_____

_____

_____

_____

_____

_____

_____

_____

_____

(Thanks)

Thanks, thanks, thanks

Reflect and be thankful for those little things you
have in your life that you take for granted.

Date:

Start here

Today I want to say thanks (God / Universe) that:

_____

_____

_____

Thanks for: _____

_____

_____

_____

_____

_____

_____

_____

_____

My to-do list which I am grateful to have:

In my life I am grateful for...

Thanks

I feel very blessed because I learned:

People I have in my heart
that make me feel happy and blessed

Thanks,
thanks,
thanks

Thanks

I Wish...

_____
_____
_____
_____
_____
_____
_____
_____
_____
_____

Thank someone who has been in your life:

Date:

Start here

Things I am grateful for:

Thanks!

Date:

Start here

Today I am grateful for:

I feel blessed because

I love being:

I love my life and I am happy because:

I would like to:

That's why Thasks the Universe/God to:

Thanks!

Date:

Start here

Today I am grateful for:

10 things I am thankful for:

I feel blessed to be:

Thanks to _____

I love my life and I am happy that:

Thanks!

>> *I feel very blessed to have:*

_____

_____

_____

*Other things that I have in my heart
that make me feel happy and blessed*

_____

_____

_____

_____

_____

_____

_____

(Thanks)

Thanks, thanks, thanks

Thanks...

_____

_____

_____

_____

_____

_____

_____

_____

_____

_____

_____

*Reflect and be thankful for those little things you
have in your life that you take for granted.*

Date:

Start here

Today I want to say thanks (God / Universe) that:

_____
_____
_____

Thanks for: _____
_____
_____
_____
_____
_____
_____

My to-do list which I am grateful to have:

In my life I am grateful for...

Thanks

I feel very blessed because I learned:

People I have in my heart
that make me feel happy and blessed

I Wish...

Thanks

Thanks,
thanks,
thanks

Thank someone who has been in your life:

Date:

Start here

Things I am grateful for:

Thanks!

Date:

Start here

Today I am grateful for:

I feel blessed because

I love being:

I love my life and I am happy because:

I would like to:

That's why Thanks the Universe/God to:

Thanks!

Date:

Start here

Today I am grateful for:

10 things I am thankful for:

I feel blessed to be:

Thanks to _____

I love my life and I am happy that:

Thanks!

I feel very blessed to have:

_____

_____

_____

_____

Other things that I have in my heart
that make me feel happy and blessed

_____

_____

_____

_____

_____

_____

_____

Thanks...

_____

_____

_____

_____

_____

_____

_____

_____

_____

_____

Thanks

Thanks, thanks, thanks

Reflect and be thankful for those little things you
have in your life that you take for granted.

Date:

Start here

Today I want to say thanks (God / Universe) that:

_____

_____

_____

_____

Thanks for: _____

_____

_____

_____

_____

_____

_____

_____

My to-do list which I am grateful to have:

In my life I am grateful for...

_____

_____

_____

Thanks

I feel very blessed because I learned:

People I have in my heart
that make me feel happy and blessed

Thanks,
thanks,
thanks

Thanks

I Wish...

Thank someone who has been in your life:

Date:

Start here

Things I am grateful for:

Thanks!

Date:

Start here

Today I am grateful for:

I feel blessed because

I love being:

I love my life and I am happy because:

I would like to:

That's why Thasks the Universe/God to:

Thanks!

Date:

Start here

Today I am grateful for: _____

_____

_____

_____

10 things I am thankful for:

I feel blessed to be:

Thanks to _____

I love my life and I am happy that:

Thanks!

I feel very blessed to have:

_____

_____

_____

Other things that I have in my heart
that make me feel happy and blessed

_____

_____

_____

_____

_____

_____

Thanks

Thanks, thanks, thanks

Thanks...

_____

_____

_____

_____

_____

_____

_____

_____

_____

_____

Reflect and be thankful for those little things you
have in your life that you take for granted.

Date:

Start here

Today I want to say thanks (God / Universe) that:

_____

_____

_____

Thanks for: _____

_____

_____

_____

_____

_____

_____

_____

My to-do list which I am grateful to have:

In my life I am grateful for...

Thanks

I feel very blessed because I learned:

People I have in my heart
that make me feel happy and blessed

Thanks,
thanks,
thanks

Thanks

I Wish...

Thank someone who has been in your life:

Date:

Things I am grateful for:

Thanks!

Date:

Start here

Today I am grateful for:

I feel blessed because

I love being:

I love my life and I am happy because:

I would like to:

That's why Thasks the Universe/God to:

Thanks!

Date:

Start here

Today I am grateful for:

10 things I am thankful for:

I feel blessed to be:

Thanks to _____

I love my life and I am happy that:

Thanks!

I feel very blessed to have:

_____

_____

_____

Other things that I have in my heart
that make me feel happy and blessed

_____

_____

_____

_____

_____

_____

_____

Thanks

Thanks, thanks, thanks

Thanks...

_____

_____

_____

_____

_____

_____

_____

_____

_____

_____

_____

Reflect and be thankful for those little things you
have in your life that you take for granted.

Date: _____

Start here

Today I want to say thanks (God / Universe) that: _____

_____
_____
_____
_____

Thanks for: _____
_____
_____
_____
_____
_____
_____
_____

My to-do list which I am grateful to have:

_____
_____
_____
_____
_____
_____
_____
_____
_____
_____
_____
_____
_____
_____
_____
_____

In my life I am grateful for...

_____
_____
_____

Thanks

I feel very blessed because I learned:

People I have in my heart
that make me feel happy and blessed

Thanks,
thanks,
thanks

Thanks

I Wish...

_____
_____
_____
_____
_____
_____
_____
_____
_____

Thank someone who has been in your life:

Date:

Start here

Things I am grateful for:

Thanks!

Date:

Start here

Today I am grateful for:

I feel blessed because

I love being:

I love my life and I am happy because:

I would like to:

That's why Thasks the Universe/God to:

Thanks!

Date: _____

Start here

Today I am grateful for: _____
_____
_____
_____

10 things I am thankful for:

I feel blessed to be:
_____
_____
_____
_____
_____
_____
_____

Thanks to _____

I love my life and I am happy that:
_____
_____
_____
_____

Thanks!

I feel very blessed to have:

_____

_____

_____

Other things that I have in my heart that make me feel happy and blessed

_____

_____

_____

_____

_____

Thanks

Thanks, thanks, thanks

Thanks...

_____

_____

_____

_____

_____

_____

_____

_____

_____

_____

_____

Reflect and be thankful for those little things you have in your life that you take for granted.

Date: _____

Start here

Today I want to say thanks (God / Universe) that: _____

_____
_____
_____
_____

Thanks for: _____
_____
_____
_____
_____
_____
_____
_____

In my life I am grateful for...
_____
_____
_____

My to-do list which I am grateful to have:
_____
_____
_____
_____
_____
_____
_____
_____
_____
_____
_____

Thanks

I feel very blessed because I learned:

_____

_____

_____

_____

People I have in my heart
that make me feel happy and blessed

Thanks,
thanks,
thanks

Thanks

I Wish...

_____

_____

_____

_____

_____

_____

_____

_____

_____

_____

Thank someone who has been in your life:

Date:

Start here

Things I am grateful for:

Thanks!

Date:

Start here

Today I am grateful for:

I feel blessed because

I love being:

I love my life and I am happy because:

I would like to:

That's why Thasks the Universe/God to:

Thanks!

Date:

Start here

Today I am grateful for: _____

10 things I am thankful for:

I feel blessed to be:

Thanks to _____

I love my life and I am happy that:

Thanks!

I feel very blessed to have:

_____

_____

_____

_____

Other things that I have in my heart
that make me feel happy and blessed

_____

_____

_____

_____

_____

_____

Thanks...

_____

_____

_____

_____

_____

_____

_____

_____

_____

_____

_____

Thanks

Thanks, thanks, thanks

Reflect and be thankful for those little things you
have in your life that you take for granted.

Date:

Start here

Today I want to say thanks (God / Universe) that:

_____
_____
_____
_____

Thanks for: _____
_____
_____
_____
_____
_____
_____

My to-do list which I am grateful to have:

In my life I am grateful for...

Thanks

I feel very blessed because I learned:

_____

_____

_____

People I have in my heart
that make me feel happy and blessed

Thanks,
thanks,
thanks

Thanks

I Wish...

_____

_____

_____

_____

_____

_____

_____

_____

_____

Thank someone who has been in your life:

Date:

Things I am grateful for:

Thanks!

Date:

Start here

Today I am grateful for:

I feel blessed because

I love being:

I love my life and I am happy because:

I would like to:

That's why Thanks the Universe/God to:

Thanks!

Date:

Start here

Today I am grateful for: _____

10 things I am thankful for:

I feel blessed to be:
_____
_____
_____
_____
_____
_____
_____
_____

Thanks to _____

I love my life and I am happy that:

Thanks!

I feel very blessed to have:

Other things that I have in my heart that make me feel happy and blessed

_____

_____

_____

_____

_____

_____

Thanks, thanks, thanks

Thanks

Thanks...

_____

_____

_____

_____

_____

_____

_____

_____

_____

Reflect and be thankful for those little things you have in your life that you take for granted.

Date:

Start here

Today I want to say thanks (God / Universe) that:

_____

_____

_____

_____

Thanks for: _____

_____

_____

_____

_____

_____

_____

_____

My to-do list which I am grateful to have:

In my life I am grateful for...

_____

_____

_____

_____

Thanks

I feel very blessed because I learned:

_____

_____

_____

_____

People I have in my heart
that make me feel happy and blessed

Thanks,
thanks,
thanks

Thanks

I Wish...

_____

_____

_____

_____

_____

_____

_____

_____

_____

_____

_____

Thank someone who has been in your life:

Date:

Things I am grateful for:

Thanks!

Date:

Start here

Today I am grateful for:

I feel blessed because

I love being:

I love my life and I am happy because:

I would like to:

That's why Thasks the Universe/God to:

Thanks!

Date:

Today I am grateful for:

10 things I am thankful for:

I feel blessed to be:

Thanks to _____

I love my life and I am happy that:

Start here

Thanks!

❯❯ I feel very blessed to have:

_____

_____

_____

Other things that I have in my heart
that make me feel happy and blessed

_____

_____

_____

_____

_____

_____

_____

(Thanks)

Thanks, thanks, thanks

Thanks...

_____

_____

_____

_____

_____

_____

_____

_____

_____

_____

_____

Reflect and be thankful for those little things you
have in your life that you take for granted.

Date:

Start here

Today I want to say thanks (God / Universe) that:

_____

_____

_____

_____

Thanks for: _____

_____

_____

_____

_____

_____

_____

My to-do list which I am grateful to have:

In my life I am grateful for...

_____

_____

_____

Thanks

I feel very blessed because I learned:

_____

_____

_____

_____

People I have in my heart
that make me feel happy and blessed

Thanks,
thanks,
thanks

Thanks

I Wish...

_____
_____
_____
_____
_____
_____
_____
_____
_____
_____
_____

Thank someone who has been in your life:

Date:

Start here

Things I am grateful for:

Thanks!

Date:

Start here

Today I am grateful for:

I feel blessed because

I love being:

I love my life and I am happy because:

I would like to:

That's why Thasks the Universe/God to:

Thanks!

Date:

Today I am grateful for: _____
_____
_____
_____

10 things I am thankful for:

I feel blessed to be:
_____
_____
_____
_____
_____
_____
_____

Start here

Thanks to _____

I love my life and I am happy that:
_____
_____
_____
_____

Thanks!

I feel very blessed to have:

_____

_____

_____

Other things that I have in my heart that make me feel happy and blessed

_____

_____

_____

_____

_____

_____

Thanks

Thanks, thanks, thanks

Thanks...

_____

_____

_____

_____

_____

_____

_____

_____

_____

_____

_____

Reflect and be thankful for those little things you have in your life that you take for granted.

Date:

Today I want to say thanks (God / Universe) that:

Start here

Thanks for: _____

_____

_____

_____

_____

_____

_____

_____

My to-do list which
I am grateful to have:

In my life I am grateful for...

Thanks

I feel very blessed because I learned:

People I have in my heart
that make me feel happy and blessed

I Wish...

Thanks,
thanks,
thanks

Thanks

Thank someone who has been in your life:

Date:

Start here

Things I am grateful for:

Thanks!

Date:

Start here

Today I am grateful for:

I feel blessed because

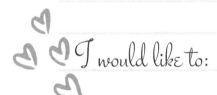 I love being:

I love my life and I am happy because:

I would like to:

That's why Thanks the Universe/God to:

Thanks!

Date:

Start here

Today I am grateful for:
_____
_____
_____

10 things I am thankful for:

I feel blessed to be:
_____
_____
_____
_____
_____
_____
_____
_____

Thanks to _____

I love my life and I am happy that:
_____
_____
_____

Thanks!

I feel very blessed to have:

_____

_____

_____

_____

Other things that I have in my heart
that make me feel happy and blessed

_____

_____

_____

_____

_____

_____

Thanks...

_____

_____

_____

_____

_____

_____

_____

_____

_____

_____

Thanks

Thanks, thanks, thanks

Reflect and be thankful for those little things you
have in your life that you take for granted.

Date:

Start here

Today I want to say thanks (God / Universe) that:

_____
_____
_____
_____

Thanks for: _____

_____
_____
_____
_____
_____
_____
_____

My to-do list which I am grateful to have:

In my life I am grateful for...

Thanks

I feel very blessed because I learned:

_____

_____

_____

_____

People I have in my heart
that make me feel happy and blessed

I Wish...

_____

_____

_____

_____

_____

_____

_____

_____

_____

_____

_____

Thanks,
thanks,
thanks

Thanks

Thank someone who has been in your life:

Date:

Start here

Things I am grateful for:

_____

_____

_____

_____

_____

_____

_____

_____

_____

_____

_____

_____

_____

_____

_____

_____

_____

_____

_____

_____

_____

Thanks!

Date:

Start here

Today I am grateful for:

I feel blessed because

I love being:

I love my life and I am happy because:

I would like to:

That's why Thasks the Universe/God to:

Thanks!

Date:

Start here

Today I am grateful for: _____

10 things I am thankful for:

I feel blessed to be:

Thanks to _____

I love my life and I am happy that:

Thanks!

I feel very blessed to have:

_____

_____

_____

Other things that I have in my heart
that make me feel happy and blessed

_____

_____

_____

_____

_____

_____

Thanks

Thanks, thanks, thanks

Thanks...

_____

_____

_____

_____

_____

_____

_____

_____

_____

_____

_____

Reflect and be thankful for those little things you
have in your life that you take for granted.

Date: _____

Start here

Today I want to say thanks (God / Universe) that:

_____
_____
_____
_____

Thanks for: _____
_____
_____
_____
_____
_____
_____

My to-do list which I am grateful to have:

In my life I am grateful for...

Thanks

I feel very blessed because I learned:

People I have in my heart
that make me feel happy and blessed

Thanks,
thanks,
thanks

Thanks

I Wish...

Thank someone who has been in your life:

Date:

Things I am grateful for:

Thanks!

Date:

Start here

Today I am grateful for:

I feel blessed because

I love being:

I love my life and I am happy because:

I would like to:

That's why Thanks the Universe/God to:

Thanks!

Date:

Start here

Today I am grateful for:

10 things I am thankful for:

I feel blessed to be:

Thanks to _____

I love my life and I am happy that:

Thanks!

>> *I feel very blessed to have:*

Other things that I have in my heart
that make me feel happy and blessed

Thanks...

Thanks

Thanks, thanks, thanks

Reflect and be thankful for those little things you
have in your life that you take for granted.

Date:

Start here

Today I want to say thanks (God / Universe) that:

_____
_____
_____
_____

Thanks for: _____
_____
_____
_____
_____
_____
_____
_____

My to-do list which
I am grateful to have:

In my life I am grateful for...

Thanks

I feel very blessed because I learned:

People I have in my heart
that make me feel happy and blessed

I Wish...

_____

Thanks,
thanks,
thanks

Thanks

Thank someone who has been in your life:

Date:

Start here

Things I am grateful for:

Thanks!

Date:

Start here

Today I am grateful for:

I feel blessed because

I love being:

I love my life and I am happy because:

I would like to:

That's why Thasks the Universe/God to:

Thanks!

Date:

Today I am grateful for:

Start here

10 things I am thankful for:

I feel blessed to be:

Thanks to _____

I love my life and I am happy that:

Thanks!

I feel very blessed to have:

_____

_____

_____

Other things that I have in my heart that make me feel happy and blessed

_____

_____

_____

_____

_____

Thanks...

_____

_____

_____

_____

_____

_____

_____

_____

_____

_____

Thanks

Thanks, thanks, thanks

Reflect and be thankful for those little things you have in your life that you take for granted.

Date:

Start here

Today I want to say thanks (God / Universe) that:

_____
_____
_____
_____

Thanks for: _____
_____
_____
_____
_____
_____
_____
_____
_____

My to-do list which I am grateful to have:

In my life I am grateful for...
_____
_____
_____
_____

Thanks

I feel very blessed because I learned:

People I have in my heart
that make me feel happy and blessed

Thanks,
thanks,
thanks

Thanks

I Wish...

Thank someone who has been in your life:

Date:

Start here

Things I am grateful for:

Thanks!

Date:

Start here

Today I am grateful for:

I feel blessed because

I love being:

I love my life and I am happy because:

I would like to:

That's why Thanks the Universe/God to:

Thanks!

Date:

Start here

Today I am grateful for:

10 things I am thankful for:

I feel blessed to be:

Thanks to _____

I love my life and I am happy that:

Thanks!

I feel very blessed to have:

_____

_____

_____

_____

Other things that I have in my heart
that make me feel happy and blessed

_____

_____

_____

_____

_____

_____

Thanks

Thanks, thanks, thanks

Thanks...

_____

_____

_____

_____

_____

_____

_____

_____

_____

_____

Reflect and be thankful for those little things you
have in your life that you take for granted.

Date:

Today I want to say thanks (God / Universe) that:

_____

_____

Start here

Thanks for: _____

_____

_____

_____

_____

_____

_____

_____

My to-do list which I am grateful to have:

In my life I am grateful for...

Thanks

I feel very blessed because I learned:

People I have in my heart
that make me feel happy and blessed

I Wish...

Thanks,
thanks,
thanks

Thanks

Thank someone who has been in your life:

Date:

Start here

Things I am grateful for:

Thanks!

Date:

Start here

Today I am grateful for:

I feel blessed because

I love being:

I love my life and I am happy because:

I would like to:

That's why Thasks the Universe/God to:

Thanks!

Date:

Today I am grateful for:

Start here

10 things I am thankful for:

I feel blessed to be:

Thanks to _____

I love my life and I am happy that:

Thanks!

I feel very blessed to have:

Other things that I have in my heart that make me feel happy and blessed

Thanks...

Thanks

Thanks, thanks, thanks

Reflect and be thankful for those little things you have in your life that you take for granted.

Date:

Start here

Today I want to say thanks (God / Universe) that:

_____
_____
_____

Thanks for: _____
_____
_____
_____
_____
_____
_____

My to-do list which I am grateful to have:

In my life I am grateful for...

Thanks

I feel very blessed because I learned:

People I have in my heart
that make me feel happy and blessed

Thanks,
thanks,
thanks

Thanks

I Wish...

Thank someone who has been in your life:

Date:

Start here

Things I am grateful for:

Thanks!

Date:

Start here

Today I am grateful for:

I feel blessed because

I love being:

I love my life and I am happy because:

I would like to:

That's why Thanks the Universe/God to:

Thanks!

Date:

Start here

Today I am grateful for:

10 things I am thankful for:

I feel blessed to be:

Thanks to _____

I love my life and I am happy that:

Thanks!

➤➤ I feel very blessed to have:

_____

_____

_____

Other things that I have in my heart that make me feel happy and blessed

_____

_____

_____

_____

_____

_____

➤➤

Thanks...

_____

_____

_____

_____

_____

_____

_____

_____

_____

_____

_____

_____

(Thanks)

Thanks, thanks, thanks

Reflect and be thankful for those little things you have in your life that you take for granted.

Date: _____

Start here

Today I want to say thanks (God / Universe) that:

_____

_____

_____

_____

Thanks for: _____

_____

_____

_____

_____

_____

_____

_____

My to-do list which I am grateful to have:

In my life I am grateful for...

Thanks

I feel very blessed because I learned:

People I have in my heart
that make me feel happy and blessed

Thanks,
thanks,
thanks

Thanks

I Wish...

Thank someone who has been in your life:

Date:

Start here

Things I am grateful for:

Thanks!

Date:

Start here

Today I am grateful for:

I feel blessed because

I love being:

I love my life and I am happy because:

I would like to:

That's why Thasks the Universe/God to:

Thanks!

Date:

Start here

Today I am grateful for:

10 things I am thankful for:

I feel blessed to be:

Thanks to _____

I love my life and I am happy that:

Thanks!

I feel very blessed to have:

_____

_____

_____

Other things that I have in my heart
that make me feel happy and blessed

_____

_____

_____

_____

_____

_____

_____

Thanks

Thanks, thanks, thanks

Thanks...

_____

_____

_____

_____

_____

_____

_____

_____

_____

_____

Reflect and be thankful for those little things you
have in your life that you take for granted.

Date:

Start here

Today I want to say thanks (God / Universe) that:

_____
_____
_____
_____

Thanks for: _____
_____
_____
_____
_____
_____
_____
_____

My to-do list which I am grateful to have:

In my life I am grateful for...
_____
_____
_____

Thanks

I feel very blessed because I learned:

_____

_____

_____

_____

People I have in my heart
that make me feel happy and blessed

Thanks,
thanks,
thanks

Thanks

I Wish...

_____

_____

_____

_____

_____

_____

_____

_____

_____

_____

Thank someone who has been in your life:

Date:

Start here

Things I am grateful for:

Thanks!

Date:

Start here

Today I am grateful for:

I feel blessed because

 I love being:

I love my life and I am happy because:

I would like to:

That's why Thanks the Universe/God to:

Thanks!

Date:

Start here

Today I am grateful for:

10 things I am thankful for:

I feel blessed to be:

Thanks to _____

I love my life and I am happy that:

Thanks!

❯❯ I feel very blessed to have:

_____

_____

_____

Other things that I have in my heart that make me feel happy and blessed

_____

_____

_____

_____

_____

_____

Thanks

Thanks, thanks, thanks

Thanks...

_____

_____

_____

_____

_____

_____

_____

_____

_____

_____

_____

Reflect and be thankful for those little things you have in your life that you take for granted.

Date:

Start here

Today I want to say thanks (God / Universe) that:

_____
_____
_____
_____

Thanks for: _____
_____
_____
_____
_____
_____
_____
_____

My to-do list which I am grateful to have:

In my life I am grateful for...

Thanks

I feel very blessed because I learned:

People I have in my heart
that make me feel happy and blessed

I Wish...

Thanks,
thanks,
thanks

Thanks

Thank someone who has been in your life:

Date:

Start here

Things I am grateful for:

Thanks!

Date:

Start here

Today I am grateful for:

I feel blessed because

I love being:

I love my life and I am happy because:

I would like to:

That's why Thasks the Universe/God to:

Thanks!

Date:

Start here

Today I am grateful for:

10 things I am thankful for:

I feel blessed to be:

Thanks to _____

I love my life and I am happy that:

Thanks!

I feel very blessed to have:

Other things that I have in my heart that make me feel happy and blessed

Thanks...

Thanks

Thanks, thanks, thanks

Reflect and be thankful for those little things you have in your life that you take for granted.

Date:

Today I want to say thanks (God / Universe) that:

_____
_____
_____
_____

Start here

Thanks for: _____
_____
_____
_____
_____
_____
_____
_____

My to-do list which I am grateful to have:

In my life I am grateful for...

Thanks

I feel very blessed because I learned:

People I have in my heart
that make me feel happy and blessed

Thanks,
thanks,
thanks

Thanks

I Wish...

Thank someone who has been in your life:

Date:

Start here

Things I am grateful for:

Thanks!

Date:

Start here

Today I am grateful for:

I feel blessed because

 I love being:

I love my life and I am happy because:

I would like to:

That's why Thasks the Universe/God to:

Thanks!

Date:

Start here

Today I am grateful for:

10 things I am thankful for:

I feel blessed to be:

Thanks to _____

I love my life and I am happy that:

Thanks!

⮞⮞ I feel very blessed to have:

Other things that I have in my heart that make me feel happy and blessed

Thanks...

Thanks

Thanks, thanks, thanks

Reflect and be thankful for those little things you have in your life that you take for granted.

Date:

Start here

Today I want to say thanks (God / Universe) that:

Thanks for:

My to-do list which
I am grateful to have:

In my life I am grateful for...

Thanks

I feel very blessed because I learned:

People I have in my heart
that make me feel happy and blessed

I Wish...

Thanks,
thanks,
thanks

Thanks

Thank someone who has been in your life:

Date:

Things I am grateful for:

Start here

Thanks!

Date:

Start here

Today I am grateful for:

I feel blessed because

I love being:

I love my life and I am happy because:

I would like to:

That's why Thasks the Universe/God to:

Thanks!

Date:

Start here

Today I am grateful for:

10 things I am thankful for:

I feel blessed to be:

Thanks to _____

I love my life and I am happy that:

Thanks!

I feel very blessed to have:

Other things that I have in my heart
that make me feel happy and blessed

Thanks...

Thanks

Thanks, thanks, thanks

Reflect and be thankful for those little things you
have in your life that you take for granted.

Date:

Start here

Today I want to say thanks (God / Universe) that:

_____
_____
_____
_____

Thanks for: _____
_____
_____
_____
_____
_____
_____
_____

My to-do list which I am grateful to have:

In my life I am grateful for...
_____
_____
_____

Thanks

I feel very blessed because I learned:

People I have in my heart
that make me feel happy and blessed

Thanks,
thanks,
thanks

Thanks

I Wish...

Thank someone who has been in your life:

Date:

Start here

Things I am grateful for:

Thanks!

Date:

Start here

Today I am grateful for:

I feel blessed because

I love being:

I love my life and I am happy because:

I would like to:

That's why Thasks the Universe/God to:

Thanks!

Date:

Start here

Today I am grateful for: _____
_____
_____
_____

10 things I am thankful for:

I feel blessed to be:
_____
_____
_____
_____
_____
_____
_____

Thanks to _____

I love my life and I am happy that:
_____
_____
_____
_____

Thanks!

I feel very blessed to have:

_____

_____

_____

Other things that I have in my heart that make me feel happy and blessed

_____

_____

_____

_____

_____

_____

_____

Thanks

Thanks, thanks, thanks

Thanks...

_____

_____

_____

_____

_____

_____

_____

_____

_____

_____

Reflect and be thankful for those little things you have in your life that you take for granted.

Date:

Start here

Today I want to say thanks (God / Universe) that:

_____
_____
_____
_____

Thanks for: _____
_____
_____
_____
_____
_____
_____
_____

My to-do list which I am grateful to have:

In my life I am grateful for...

Thanks

I feel very blessed because I learned:

People I have in my heart
that make me feel happy and blessed

Thanks,
thanks,
thanks

Thanks

I Wish...

Thank someone who has been in your life:

Date:

Start here

Things I am grateful for: _____

Thanks!

Made in the USA
Las Vegas, NV
05 June 2023